MW00615110

Copyright © 2013 by theNewerYork Press LLC

Editor: Joshua S. Raab
Managing Editor: Chuck Young
Editors-at-Large: Daniel Bullard-Bates, Michelle Favin, Jared Frieder,
Colin Montgomery

Cover image by Paul Richard
Book design by Nils Davey, nilsdavey.com

Book III
Edition 1

Direct all permissions and publicity requests to media@theNewerYork.com
ISBN: 978-0-9890926-7-8

Printed in Canada by the Friesens Corporation

theNewerYork Press publishes experimental fiction in print and online.
We want to end the triumvirate of short-stories, poetry, and novels; we want
to explore new and forgotten literary forms. You are holding a collection of
our choice selections, usually two pages or less. This project is funded on
Kickstarter.com and our submissions come from writers and artists all over
the world. Welcome to theNewerYork.

 : tNYPress
theNewerYork.com

1507 7th Street, Suite 529, Santa Monica, CA 90401

a superficial hubbub
lies submerged under
unity in our time,

— MARSHALL MCLUHAN

There is a real, living

as in any other, but it

of sensation.

Disclaimer:

[Read slowly to avoid complications, read entirely. You won't like some of this work] ~~The artwork and literature in this volume will take over your internal narrative for a bit. All books do this. However throughout this fragmented text, at various points or disjunctions between stories, you may find the voice in your head struggling to transition between narrators, say a teenage girl in love and then suddenly a German soldier with his troops. The effect is disorienting and perhaps uncomfortable~~ *[This is intended; enjoy the various ghosts that can inhabit your thoughts.]*

Note. on book III:
  it's about time

      - jœR

1.

John didn't know what was happening. One minute he was in the library reading. The next he was stuttering. A pentecostal fire rose up from his groin and the tongues were crawling up his throat. He didn't even know what he was trying to say.

'Come on, cough it out,' a friend said. *'People are staring.'*

And he did. First a hand and a head and then whole bodies. They pulled themselves out of his spluttering gullet.

'We come in peace,' they said and walked away.
John lay dead on the floor.

2.

John was writing and then solving his own crossword. *'Two Across-seven letters: Oliver, part of us, wants more.'* He chuckled. The answer was a bit too obvious. But it was only 6:30, the beginning of his writing day.

His wife would be up soon. John opened the window in his study and lit up a cigarette, sticking his head right out the window. The air was a little chilly. He pulled his scarf tighter around his neck. He took a swig of black coffee from his writer's cup. The alien death-ray took his head off his shoulders so fast, he was still exhaling fumes when he landed.

3.

We know they came early in our history, just at that branch in evolution where things could have gone either way. We were barely more than monkeys then, with some fine motor skills and a few guttural noises at our disposal. The parasites came and everything changed. One monkey said to another *'I found your drawing on the cave-wall and I think it's highly derivative.'* The dumb monkey bashed the more eloquent monkey over the head with a dusty bone and used his brains for finger paint. That sent the gossips gibbering. The parasites spread and multiplied.

4. There are not many of us left now. Nobody knows how many. Most have retreated into a solitary, etiolated existence. There are pockets of us that gather and dream of taking the planet back. But it's hard to organise any kind of resistance. We use charades to communicate and base our plans on well known science-fiction movies, just so everyone has an easy point of reference.

Right now it's John's turn. Two words, first word, four syllables, first syllable–John starts hopping around on one foot, with one hand sticking up above his head and patting his empty mouth with the flat palm of the other. Independence Day. I've got the answer already but I can't say it.

5. After days of planning we find one that's workable. We will take them down one by one–divide and conquer. We will kill the auxiliaries. Then we kill the adverbs. And then we kill the conjunctions. We kill definite articles, we kill pronouns. Kill nouns. *Kill.*

UNHERALDED MONSTERS

Instead of just renting a bouncy castle, ordering pizza, and forcing his alcoholic uncle to tell war stories again, Joe decided to have a make-your-own-monster themed eighth birthday party this year. Here are the creations that arose from this event:

The Cob: Half corn-on-the-cob, half human. Jimmy made up this particular monster when he got stuck boiling corn instead of getting to play with the other kids for reasons he still doesn't understand.

Hobbies: Having his husk peeled, growing by means of photosynthesis, Franz Kafka.

Fears: Hot water, pestilence, intimacy.

The Giant Rock: Stephen created this particular creature, who, as the name implies, is an absolutely humongous rock. That can also fly. Stephen was told he didn't really 'get' the theme of the party.

Hobbies: Being immobile (except when he flies), having a really hard shell, letting people climb all over him.

Fears: Acid rain, flying, the all-eroding nature of time.

The Minotaur II: Like the other Minotaur, just taller or hairier. Made up half-heartedly by Zach (who's 'just not really into this stuff') during the party.

Hobbies: Eating I guess, like whatever bulls do, and maybe video games.

Fears: I'm bored of this shit; can we just leave?

The Emperor of Pine Trees: Created by Stephanie when she went for a walk in the forest, the Emperor of Pine Trees is her way of dealing with the all-consuming boredom that overwhelmed her by being the only girl at Joe's birthday party for the fifth year running.

Hobbies: Blending into a bunch of pine trees, releasing a woodsy aroma, scaring kids breathless.

Fears: Deforestation, pine beetles, clowns.

The Soul Crusher: Ethan dreamt this one up not as a physical punisher, but rather a beast that erodes children's sense of wonder and innocence over time through belittling comments, petty public embarrassment, and getting into overly venomous fights with Ethan's soccer coach.

Hobbies: Blaming it on your mother, making comparisons between you and your brother, forcing you to go to the birthday parties of its boss' weird son.

Fears: Being incorrect, truly loving something in this world, technology.

Hear the words, *"Die in a napalm fire."*

Fall in love with Martini.

Laugh nervously and think of suicide.

Listen to her as she says,
"For the longest time I was scared you didn't like me."

Tell her, *"I'm scared still I think."*

Text Martini, *"im going to beat the shit out of u"*

Read her response, *"make me black and blue"*

Wake up at five AM and feel nothing.

Think,
"You know this is a mistake but you're going to do it anyway,"
in response to **absolutely nothing.**

Think, "Martini kills puppies" over and over

Think, *"Martini kills puppies."* over and over.

Think, *"Martini kills puppies,"* over and over.

Feel the emptiness that permanently resides in man's abdomen.

Remember hearing about Martini jerking off two guys at once.

Build a vagina in the sandbox at the park.

Read Martini's text, *"i dont miss you"*

Wear those light up sneakers that make you run faster.

Text Martini two weeks later, *"why are u such a bitch???"*
Read her response, *"fuck off"*

Think, *"I love this person."*

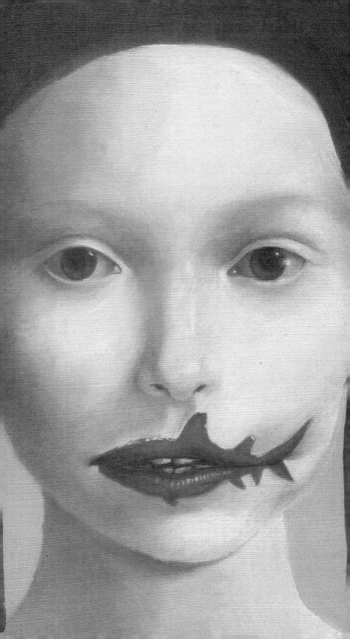

november air, over the honking cars on US 41 and into the lonely sewers, where the city shifts under the weight of ten thousand chevy impalas. decide that the cold is okay. watch as the little woman behind the counter demonstrates with her hands. the plant opens and closes its leaves depending on the light, like it's praying. open, close, open, close. listen as she explains that prayer plants are very popular among young bohemians. wonder if you are a young bohemian. porcelain panda to live under its bedroom floor. dispose of them unceremoniously. follow instructions diligently. wonder, in a moment of unpoetic justice, if this is what they've been praying for. look into the weary eyes of porcelain panda and say you're very sorry. count the spidercracks in your ceiling. sleep for twelve and a half hours. dream in tangents of dripping laughter and skyblue and burgundy and things whispered under flannel. the air conditioner is up too high. let your hands find each other for warmth.

Squares

Jane Huffman

how to kill a bonsai tree: acknowledge that you didn't get your heart broken, not really. pick up the great gatsby again. watch a documentary film on miniature gardening and realize that your new passion is miniature gardening. ask siri where you can buy a bonsai tree. drive thirty-two miles to a two-car garage off of the interstate with "bonsai house" painted on the roof. tuck your fingers into the sleeves of your sweater. throw caution to the wind. watch it flutter in the dirty November air, over the honking

pay twenty-two dollars for a bonsai tree starter kit and ninety-nine cents for a tiny porcelain panda to live under its branches. for good luck, the woman says. drive home with a prayer plant in the passenger seat. put it on your windowsill. stay awake until all the leaves are closed, engaged in prayer or photosynthesis or something. panic when it rejects its new home. call your dad. notice a growing pile of tiny, shivering, gray hands, in withered fists, scattered on your bedroom floor

to·ma·toes/tə'mātōz/: nobody says tomahtos

Che·Gue·ver·a/CHā/gə'värə/: rare Brazilian Cheese

ab·stract ·art/ab'strakt/ärt/: when "I don't get it" is kind of, like, getting it

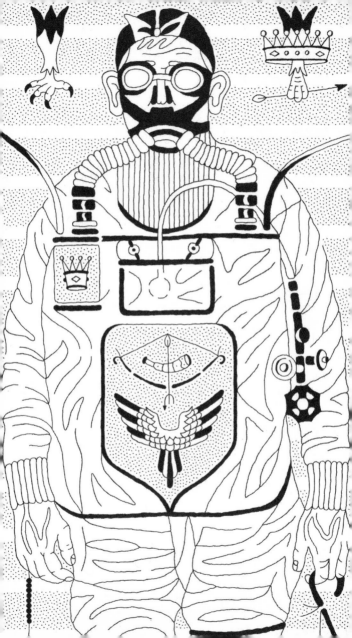

Flipbook

by

Christine

Gosny

Dearest Darling,
I had to dash up to the store today for more paper,
Hope I haven't missed your call! My corkscrew,
My flashy peacock, my long-necked bottle blue.
Every morning I write "Fly a-love to my dearest darling"
And other trash like that in permanent ink
On a paper aeroplane and throw it north to you.
I've got a book of designs. Some are shit. Some fly incredible.
Uh oh, delivery fellows are spinning out in the puddle of white wings
Wadded at the bottom of driveway. Waving their fists at me.

* IF WE WERE SHUT IN AN UNBEARABLE BLACK
AND WHITE CARTOON

Addressee: CAD/RATFINK/KNAVE at [redacted]
Mickey D told me
All about your strutting in town.
Has you pegged the pledge and tip
Of Bleecker street! I slap you
About with this two-tone glove.
The sound it makes as it hits
Your brazen cheek is the
'Bone slide of my own bloody -
Farewell! A tree grows in place
Of my ache for you. Highball in hand.
Muscles on my legs from all the pacing.
What's coming? The sound
Of children being born early. Getting gone.

* IF WE WERE PARAMOUNT STUDIO
CONTRACTS IN THE '30'S

Baby [hardandcut4lovelicks@singlesdance.co.uk],
Last night I shotgunned some Old Healer in the shower
And I thought of your mouth's left side, the bit where it
Crinkles, and came so many times I dropped the bottle.
A love bomb. This morning I was cleaning up the glass, I cut myself
On the side of my foot and the blood made me cum again
Because it reminded me of the inside of your mouth,
Left and right, when you're breathing on me like a window
You're trying to fog up so you can draw a picture.
I am your picture. Draw me closer. Draw me inside you.

* IF WE WERE SOMEWHAT NASTY CHARACTERS
IN AN EROTIC TRILOGY. ~~PART~~ 2.
                              BOOK

My petit prince,
I dreamt you into this great experience I was having
Last night. I put you in a middle seat where you could love it.
The ceiling has great acoustic promise and the plush seats are crimson.
Only a little gum and/or popcorn around. Easygoing place.
It was an auditorium full of trees, and the trees were women.
The skinny ones were saplings and the tallest were old live oaks.
A great, large man, with a head like Balzac's, stood at a podium,
Blowing out of massive cheeks and lips puckered like
The anus of a balloon. A wild wind went unfettered through
The hall. The women went "aaaahh!" A little like a giggle,
A little like a worry. They all fell down into cinnamon roll
Or twig poses and swept across the floor. Their outfits
Were gold and shiny. Some tried to cover themselves at the
Breast and pubis mons, but we saw everything. I tried
To hold you but you had leaned forward on the back
Of the seat in front of you, arms crossed, grinning,
And probably choosing one for later. I saw her wave.

* IF WE WERE EVEN ALLOWED TO BE ARTISTS

Christine Gosnay

Dear John,
The acorn stands at equinox.
On point. Brave, ruddy. A little warrior's cap
Rests on top for some reason. [Squirrels. Lagomorphs.]
The sun arrives like it's time to abdicate.
Which equinox is this that you have picked?
Before you pitch over, I would like to
Introduce you to this mighty oak.
He's not your father.
If you get persuasive and
convince someone to cut him open you'll see
All the things he wrote. It's not in code or even some
Indo-European language. It's just rings and rings of
Paper planes he'll have to make for somebody sad.
These eighty years were long.
In a minute, we'll be able to tell which one.
Close your eyes. Are you getting warmer?

* IF WE WERE IN THAT CARTOON AGAIN.
IN COLOR THIS TIME.

About the author:

Blast has been amazing people for years. His record for the world's longest card trick still stands. Now this famous manipulator offers you a choice selection of his most delightful magic tricks, all carefully explained and simplified with the beginner in mind. You need not practice for hours. This is magic even you can do!

THE AMAZING STICKING QUARTER

Effect

This trick never fails to startle and amuse. You display a quarter for everyone to see and, bringing it to your forehead, you make several mystic passes with your hand. After the last pass, you reveal that the quarter is stuck to your forehead.

You bow, and the quarter does not fall off. You may jump up and down, and the quarter does not fall off. You may bend over backwards across a chair, laughing and kicking, and still the quarter does not fall off.

Next, to the amazement of everyone, you may challenge members of your audience to remove the quarter. Come one and all, ladies and gentlemen, they cannot pull it off, though they tug their mightiest.

Truly, you must be a wonder worker!

Method

Like many great mysteries, the secret of the quarter is ingeniously simple. All you need is a quarter and a twopenny screw. The head of the screw is welded to the back of the quarter, an easy and inexpensive task for any metalworking shop. The screw itself can be procured for a few cents.

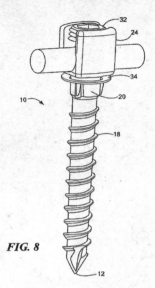

FIG. 8

Display the ungimmicked face of the quarter to the audience, then bring it to your forehead. Your mystic passes should be done with a circular motion while maintaining steady contact with the coin, which facilitates the screw's entry.

Once the quarter is in place, you may indulge in any gyrations desired or submit to the collective efforts of the audience. They will never succeed because they will always try to pull the quarter away from you.

It will not occur to people to twist in the same plane as your head. It's never happened to me.

BLAST Productions

Blast is in the middle of a 24 city radio magic tour. Check your local listings!

Homes of the wicked and the just

The house of the wicked shall be [destro]yed: but the tabernacles of the just [shall flour]ish.

The way to death

There is a way which seemeth just [to a man]: but the ends thereof lead to death.

Laughter and sorrow

Laughter shall be mingled with [sorrow: and] mourning taketh hold of the end of [joy.]

The foolish and the good

A fool shall be filled with his ow[n ways, and] the good man shall be above him.

The innocent and the discreet

The innocent believeth every [word: the dis]creet man considereth his steps.

The deceitful son and wise servant

[No] good shall come to the dec[eitful son: but] the wise servant shall prosper [in his dealing,] and his way shall be made str[aight.]

The wise man and the fool

A wise man feareth and decl[ineth from evil:] the fool leapeth over and is c[onfident.]

The impatient and the crafty

The impatient man shall [work folly: and] the crafty man is hateful.

The childish and the prudent

The childish shall possess folly, [and the] prudent shall look for knowledge.

Fate of the wicked

The evil shall fall down before the g[ood: and] the wicked before the gates of the just.

The poor and the rich

The poor man shall be hateful even to his [own] neighbor: but the friends of the rich [are] many.

Hatred and mercy

He that despiseth his neighbor, sinneth: [but] he that showeth mercy to the poor, shall [be] blessed. He that believeth in the Lord [loveth] mercy.

Evil and truth

They err that work evil: but mercy and [truth] prepare good things.

Labor and talk

In much work there shall be abundance: [but] where there are many words, there is [often]times want.

The wise and the foolish

24 The crown of the wise is their ric[hes:] the folly of fools, imprudence.

Witnesses

25 A faithful witness delivereth souls: [and] the double dealer uttereth lies.

Fear of the Lord

26 In the fear of the Lord is confidenc[e of] strength, and there shall be hope for his c[hild]ren. 27 The fear of the Lord is a foun[tain] of life, to decline from the ruin of death.

Dignity and dishonor

28 In the multitude of people is the dig[nity] of the king: and in the small number of p[eop]le the dishonor of the prince.

Patience and impatience

[2]9 He that is patient is governed with m[uch wis]dom: but he that is impatient exalteth [his folly.]

Envy

[30] Soundness of heart is the life of the fle[sh:] but envy is the rottenness of the bones.

Oppression and pity

[31] He that oppresseth the poor upbraid[eth his Mak]er: but he that hath pity on the p[oor honoreth] him.

The wicked and the just

[32 T]he wicked man shall be driven out in [his] [wicke]dness: but the just hath hope in his de[ath.]

The prudent and the ignorant

33 In the heart of the prudent resteth [wisdo]m, and it shall instruct all the ignorant.

Justice and sin

[34] Justice exalteth a nation: but sin mal[keth nat]ions miserable.

The anger of a king

35 A wise servant is acceptable to the k[ing:] he that is good for nothing shall feel his an[ger.]

CHAPTER 15

Good and foolish words

A MILD answer breaketh wrath: bu[t a] harsh word stirreth up fury. 2 [The] tongue of the wise adorneth knowledge: [but] the mouth of fools bubbleth out folly. 3 [The] eyes of the Lord in every place behold[eth the] good and the evil. 4 A peaceable tongu[e is] a tree of life: but that which is immode[rate] shall crush the spirit.

Instruction and reproof

5 A fool laugheth at the instruction of [his]

CATHOLIC CHURCH LAUNCHES CAMPAIGN TO
APPEAL TO TODAY'S YOUTH

1. Launch of "iCatholic" app that automatically books user's pew, walks user through the set up of online tithing, and periodically reminds user that God sees everything.

2. Launch of advocacy campaign to get kids "exorcismcizing" encourages youth to "Cast out the devil and simple carbs!"

3. Introduction of "Cathlickers," papal seal ring pops for kids, proves bafflingly controversial in America.

4. New line of InScentz perfumes. Scents like Frankincense and Holy Water are a hit. Abstinence, which is odorless, proves unpopular.

5. "Try Your CathLuck!" scratch-off tickets huge success after winner in Milwaukee is forgiven two deadly sins.

6. New depictions of the Holy Virgin, now clothed in a chic blue bandage dress, show that she actually looked remarkably like Katy Perry.

7. Vatican retains Hollywood talent to make the catchphrase "Hush Nun!" happen. Casts of Glee and the Modern Housewives now routinely trump disobedient female characters with hilarious zinger. "Hush Nun!" baby tee shirt line booms. Official protest by American nuns greeted by Church authorities with "flapping mouth" hand gesture and wordless lifting of cassocks to display underlying tee-shirt slogan.

8. As an olive branch to progressives and with great fanfare, the Church issues a white paper that publicly acknowledges the existence of vaginas.

Do you draw your .s or dot them? Which fonts&margins&templates do you use? & vs. and? How many ! do you put in an interrobang? #Impact #font

Every cell's a caterpillar and your muscles are just a mass of suction-cup feet stuck to accordion bodies, and they breath together #bugged

She has always liked #candy that looks like things. –Better if a waxy bottle has real liquid gooze. Who is to say it's #fake, your retainer?

Short but not detailed: one-toned, tips not done, brown, sheen like a seal, but shake it off if wet #tips #fetch #whoareyoucallingfluffy #gr

How did your hair get in my hairs? See how tightly mine is twisted #DNA and how loose #losing you are –Your curls are bouncy but I'm #winning

RT: Re-use skin as a blanket for old houses. Flakes to fall from the fan when you turn it on #confetti Leave dandruff everywhere you travel.

Color me comfy: mummify me in stitches, then pack on fibers, threads and a sweater. I'm comfortable suffocating in spider silks. I bundled.

I need an ink so I'll make some from a blood faucet or bug facet or berry fluid. In every letter I write there's blueberry skin or antenna.

Twitterature   21

g

u   g

j   l

hand   e

hand

g

playin   catch

SOOTHE AS EXCALIBUR

I'm gonna draw comics for the **prestige.** *Not for me. But for those all over guys just like me, for every glimpse of doubt, for that stand-still paralysis and the way those moments can convince you something is missing . . . And something is always missing. If I can, I'll draw that on paper because it's the one thing I might tell myself if I could go back in time. Because of all the people starving out there. And Yoga classes won't help. Going back to school* **won't help.** *Macrobiotic food* **won't help.** *A cuter girlfriend* **won't help,** *not necessarily. More money* **won't help** *either. You gotta give yourself that grand purpose, and it can be anything, in fact, the more trivial the better. But you have to weld yourself to it, some big idea, to the exclusion of all else. Because like anyone,* **like everyone,** *probably, I still waver in and out from that feeling of being doomed to live on the outside. Man, I want to draw comics the way you'd ascend to the cloud-ringed summit of a mystical mountain. And the God's truth is that* **you forget** *about getting to the top.* **You forget** *what you thought you wanted.* **You can pretend** *it makes you different, but deep-down, to your great relief, you begin to simply pray for just one good day after another . . .*

Or at least this is what I'd tell myself while taking shits when I worked the Annex Bookstore on Fulton Street. It was because of those vaulted, operatic ceilings in the bathroom, and I could always hear a faint surge, like applause, from the foot-traffic on the cobblestones outside. Tiled floors and brass spigots, bathroom of champions. And I'd walk out shadowboxing, past the full-length mirrors down the corridor.

Sometimes the most productive thing a person can do is go to sleep.

-BENJAMIN WOLFE

MY DELICATE RESPONSE TO A CHILD'S WRITING PROMPT WEBSITE.

If one day animals really could talk I'd ask them about their children, about why the green moon has massive legs, who their accomplices are, who the animal spokesmen is, do they know that we think they see everything, what are their laws and customs and what would happen if I broke those laws and customs, which animals speak Irish, French, Italian, Spanish or American. I let one of them rinse off in my bathing cup. That's what I'd ask if animals could talk.

If there were no television I'd beach my television set down within the dunes, I'd retire from life and build a halfway house at Heliopolis, I'd become infatuated with airports, I'd go sit sideways on the settee and eat ginger biscuits, pining for the TV, I'd purchase a yacht and shade my walk up and down the bridge deck, grabbing a box of matches and striking a light.

If a famous person came to visit my home I'd practice a curse, placing a portentous cataclysm to hang over his destiny, I'd push him into the swimming pool, making him a white blob bobbing on the water, sunrays would suddenly reveal the famous person in stark loneliness, I'd ask him what the big deal about Hollywood is and why weren't the black walls and sneering revolution digging away at his insides.

**Get Lost in the Electric Encyclopedia
of Experimental Literature.**

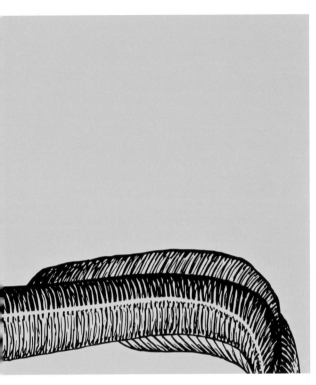

theNewerYork.com/eeel

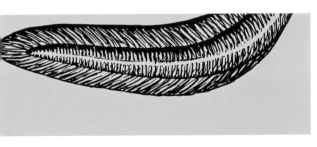

I AM GOING TO PUT ON A PAIR OF JEANS

I am going to put on a pair of white jeans and you are going to push me down the stairs

I am going to put on a pair of black jeans and you are going to roll over my toes with your car on accident

I am going to put on a pair of blue jeans and you are going to sell my organs on the black market to pay off your student loans

I am going to put on a pair of red jeans and you are going to watch me stare at the same website on my computer for 4 hours straight

I am going to put on a pair of yellow jeans and you are going to put my other jeans in the dryer so that they are all toasty warm and then watch me try each of them on one at a time

I am going to put on a pair of green jeans and you are going to show me a power point presentation on the dangers of sexting

I am going to put on a pair of purple jeans and you are going to drive me out to the arboretum and we are going to go for a hike and not really talk to each other that much and wonder if it's a problem

I am going to put on a pair of oversized jean shorts and you are going to take me to the pet store and we are going to look at the different puppies and consider playing with some of them but decide not to and go to a restaurant instead

I am going to put on a pair of knee high cut off shorts and you are going to ask me about a bunch of Cool Bands I have never heard of while we are riding bikes. You are going to shout unfamiliar names back at me while we are riding on the street and I am going to pretend I understand by smiling and shouting Yeah but I can't really hear you because it's too windy

I am going to put on a pair of pleated department store khaki slacks and you are going to drive me to the mall and pretend to be interested in buying a cellphone case from an overzealous salesman at a kiosk because you are lonely even though we are together

I am going to put on a pair of stiff corduroys and you are going to lower the basketball hoop on my parents driveway to six feet so we can both do slam dunks

I am going to put on a pair of long johns and you are going to try to get me into a critically acclaimed cable TV series on Netflix and I am going to do my best to feign interest

I am going to put on a pair of sweatpants and wander out into the forest in the middle of the night, in the dead of winter, with my ipod playing static on repeat, and you are going to remember me the way I wanted to be remembered: by my collective social media output

There is no need to fear the
lightning in New York City,
shoulder to shoulder with
scaffolding and fences—the
metal and concrete, roof decks
and penthouses, catch the
weight of the sky when it feels
the need to fall. The city's grid
and deadbolts protect you from
the unplanned and damn it. They
put *whim* in a cold mauve filing
cabinet to protest the unmanned
planet; they find the fruit of
youth and attempt to can it.

But out deep in the forest—the
lightning is so possible, the trees
so wet and waiting, your death is
so near—and all other things are
so very real. You remember that
all the energy in the sky—under
the weight of an angel or for no
reason at all—might empty into you.

Name: Sübyancı

Gender: Male / **Origin:** Turkish / **Meaning:** Pedophile
Pronunciation: *Süb-yan-cı*
Additional Info: The dotless "i" in the name Sübyancı indicates a "back vowel" variant of the dotted "i," in which the tongue is positioned as far back as possible in the mouth, to create a darker sound. Also dark: the name's meaning. Names that end with a dotless "i" are on the rise in over 650 countries around the world.
(TRENDY ALERT)

I should have been more specific in previous rejection — not interested in names that mean pedophile in any language

pls fact-check # of countries

Name: Monositojen

Gender: Female / **Origin:** Haitian Creole / **Meaning:** Listeria
Pronunciation: *Blah-blah-blah-Jen*
Additional Info: Monositojen is a shortened form of "Monositojennifer," as in the popular singer Monositojennifer Lopez, whose hit song, "I'm Gonna Be Alright," referred to her own battle with Listeria-induced food poisoning.
(TRENDY ALERT)

all TRENDY ALERTS need to be notarized!

names related to diarrhea-causing bacteria need prior authorization

Name: Vägglöss

Gender: Female / **Origin:** Swedish / **Meaning:** Bedbugs
Pronunciation: Vag-gloss
Additional Info: "Vägglöss, my vägglöss," is a popular Swedish lullaby.

pls confirm you received email — add'l info must have 2 seperate facts.

I know this lullaby — and it is not popular!!

Name: Chwydu

Gender: Male / **Origin:** Welsh / **Meaning:** Vomit
Pronunciation: Chewy-doo → WELSH NO LONGER ALLOWED
Additional Info: In the 1948 Olympics, Chwydu Jones won a gold medal for the Welsh nation. Chwydu was the final word in the 1979 National Scrabble Championships. Chwydu has been a name on the rise among babies born with no digestive system. (TRENDY ALERT) - MUST BE NOTARIZED!

as per freelance handbook (attached - pls read) we prefer American Scrabble Championship word lists, due to reciprocal agreement

Name: Seennakkus

Gender: Female / **Origin:** Estonian / **Meaning:** Yeast infection
Pronunciation: Just like it's spelled
Additional Info: The yeast infection is the official gynecological disease of Estonia. In the American sitcom, "Alice," the character of Flo was originally named Seennakkus before a last- minute change by the producers. For many, Seennakkus is the diminutive of Seennakkuss.

This submission is perfect — your check is in the mail. Best, Seennakkus Jones, editor

LES INNUMERABLES (A BINARY TALE)

In front of its old, grand round mirror, **2** wriggles its long, slim neck, preens the plumes at the end of its tail and gloats. *You are 2*, it smiles at its reflection; *no other can be you.*

A few blocks away, **8**, also in front of its round mirror, loosens the belt around its waist, and indulges itself in the sight of its perfect, even curves.

*Whoever sets their eyes on you and thinks that you are **4+4** or **3+5** is talking nonsense. They have no eyes to see you as an individual, independent, complete being.*

At the other end of the City, **1283** contemplates the consequences of being **1283**. *I am not an ordinary number. I am integer and prime. There is no other number that represents the concept of **1283**; I alone express this singular and solitary concept – one that blesses an equally singular and solitary being.*

Every night, countless numbers leave such thoughts and words at the feet of their mirrors – offerings to the round god who bears their figures. Then they go to bed, cross their pillows and brood their sphereal dreams: each of them unique, as is their dreamer.

Every night, when all the numbers fall asleep in the Eternal City, One visits each house and gently wipes the round mirrors clean; they, wrapped in the thick shroud of darkness, lay off the burden of their reflections – for a few hours they become, once again, small, plain noughts...

DILEMMAS OF MODERN MAN

cla·sses/klasiz/: upper, middle upper, lower upper, upper middle, middle middle, lower middle, poor

com·e·dy/ˈkämədē/: tragedy you laugh at

ox·y·mo·ron/ˌäksəˈmôrˌän/: Billy Mays

DEAR spiky things on my kidneys that make them look like medicine balls

DEAR FAVORITE WORD SLOUCH

DEAR CAN'T CHANGE MOSTLY EVERYTHING

DEAR second favorite word numbskull

DEAR LEAST FAVORITE WORD INEXCUSABLE

DEAR—

hate to say it cause i don't want to jinx it true love

DEAR catholicism

DEAR alcoholism

DEAR ATHEISM
DEAR ATHEISM

buddhism

DEAR DEAR

DEAR DEAR OPTIMISM

DEAR cynicism DEAR PRECIOUS PRECIOUS SARCASM

DEAR no matter what

DEAR maybe just maybe.

listening to a recording of cheech and chong's sister mary elephant when i was nine and laughing so hard i peed on my brother's bed

Christine Tierney   A Flash

RANDOM AND NOT SO RANDOM SALUTATIONS

DEAR heebie-jeebies and plastic blue skies

DEAR kidneys that were once the

DEAR questionable memory of getting my period my drivers license my first f in both math and science my first bag of weed and my first dive-ins all at 3:37pm on a wednesday in 1982

DEAR size of peanuts walnuts prunes

DEAR DEAR

DEAR blood test i wish i could study for and ace

DEAR staring at a zit in the mirror for so long it turns into a lumpy red potato

DEAR TAKE A DEEP BREATH AND LIVE IN THE MOMENT

DEAR FAILING MISERABLY AT

DEAR LIVING IN THE MOMENT

DEAR sacred consecrated hallowed revered divine and blessed sense of humor

1793 Ignorant African
Show you know English-answer to your "name"

1817 3/5 of a man
Show virility-show line of children, show bent back

1831 Disobedient
Show bare back, lashes on lashes

1858 Lazy
Show bare feet, calloused hands, show cotton is king

1870 Too stupid to learn
Show degree from Harvard University

1895 Too stupid to vote
Show literacy, pass test

1918 Not American
Show World War I uniform and wounds and scars

1924 Lazy
Show teeth, grin wide, traverse states as Pullman porter

1926 Too stupid to write
Show Harlem Renaissance Writers

1936 Not American
Show four gold medals at Munich Olympics

1944 Too stupid to fly planes
Show Tuskegee strength and numbers and skill

1945 Not American
Show World War II uniform and wounds and scars

1950 Too stupid to write
Show Pulitzer Prize in Poetry

1955 Lazy
Show bus pass to sit in rear (or stand) to and from work

1971 Not American
Show Vietnam uniform and wounds and scars

1993 Too stupid to write
Show Nobel Prize in Literature

2009 Lazy, stupid, not American
Show African American President of US

2011 Not American (President)
Show birth certificate (again, again, again).

Check out mah tumblr.

-Edgar Allen Poe

An Unfamous Quote

MANIFESTO FOR THAT UNFORTUNATE STAIN ON MY PANTS

1. The stain is not just a stain is not just a stain is not just a stain.

It is a strobing cherry-red CAUTION, a plaintive siren, a somnolent intercom voice, a subversively conservative Judd Apatow film, warning deli patrons, café flaneurs, and summertime strollers about the dangers of excess condiment, the unreliability of Those Damn Sippy Cup Tops, and the structural integrity issues of ice cream fleeing a wilting sun. This could be you next, infant child creature waving around that Rocket Pop like a baton, it says, if it could theoretically speak.

Some in the academy have argued, in the pages of *The Journal Of Foodstuff Deposit And Residue Studies* (JFDRS), that stains are inherently amoral, the unfortunate splash of an indifferent universe, but this fails to acknowledge Alfred Demint's groundbreaking work on the Cognitive Self-Flagellating Flaccidity theory, which I feel has conclusively proved the link between stains and subconscious intent. Stains are always and everywhere a moral phenomenon.

2. The stain dangles visions of utopia.

In his celebrated opus *The Stain As Organizing Principle,* Edible Spectrologist and Marxist historian Anthony Jacques traces the history of the stain as fundamental to the socio-economic conflicts of historical materialism, the stain itself being sort of a physical manifestation of the labor-capital divide, historically speaking. Thus, if I am reading this correctly, not until every shirt and skirt and khaki and capri are besmirched and festooned with the wraith of condiments can we forge the timeless temporal paradise, or something.

Point number two runs in direct opposition to point number one, but because I am exceedingly erudite I am incapable of detecting this. That is, unless the stain is at once reactionary and revolutionary in a sort of quantum dualism.

3. The stain must not misrepresent its community or origins.

The stain is fundamentally an expression of its muddled visage, be it neo-Marxist mustard or neo-liberal coffee.

The stain in question is an asymmetric sickly yellow splatter uncomfortably close to the crotch and all its prurient associations. A few tawny islands lie off its coastline in the otherwise murky ocean of burnt amber chinos. Consequently, my stain must not presume to speak authoritatively on the dainty dilettantism of crème fraiche.

4. Stains are not theorists.

Although the stain may bemoan the latent nihilism of a world in which poor hand-eye coordination carelessly dictates the fate of cloth—and may privately kvetch about its tragic luck with its insouciant, unvarnished neighbors—the stain should not introduce issues of agency or privilege into the conversation. The conversation is about pants.

5. Stains are not devices of upward mobility.

You do not chance upon a delectable dagger of Heinz splayed upon your thigh with dollar signs cartoonishly replacing your pupils. Stains are not a solution to long-term structural unemployment nor stagnating wages nor rising income inequality nor will they rejuvenate the American manufacturing sector. Clayton Christensen has not written a Harvard Business School case study analyzing stains through the prism of steel mills. Do not believe charlatans evangelizing to drop it all and slather your pants up in relish, as appetizing as that may sound.

6. Use less mustard next time.

REMORSE RE-MORSED:
WILLIAM SHAKESPEARE'S SONNET CVIII

Unstandardized Testing:
Section III: Unscramble[1]

Instructions: Arrange the following words into coherent questions (punctuation provided). 10 points.

1. to do do do people what Why tell us we?

2. it Is like because we do it to?

3. we want it to Is it because do?

4. Is too do it because lazy we are not to it?

5. because it Is are we scared too to do it not?

6. being doing because it Is requires?

7. combination two questions identified a through six of of the it reasons because in Is?

8. too lazy to do lazy something not you are If you are still?

9. If converse doing, is the being requires doing that being true, i.e., requires?

10. fair Is it to ask of others which that of ourselves we to ask are unwilling?

Bonus: Answer the questions.

---

1. These questions were recovered from a trash bin. The answer key was indecipherable due to severe food stains (specifically, mustard, tomato sauce, and chocolate pudding). Grader encouraged to use his or her own discretion when evaluating responses.

A Test   Zach Davidson

YOUR WILLY SO SMALL. MATE

ELL YOUR TEETH - RAW CHAIN

H DELUXE BREEDING, KISSERSXXX

NON-STOP EPIPHANY, SO SW

OWARD THE WHOLE WORLD E

YES, I MISS YOU DOUR

AN ASK YOUR SHIT OUT YOU

GROCHECK IUST IN TO WHO

SEWALOVER YES X TOLD ME A BIT.

BRING ME TO MAKE A INGR BLOOD

WHAT CAN MY CUNT

TOWARLINKING

RLY A BLINKING JUNK OUT!R

ME, I CAFINGER 4 SURE OUR

OMPULSIVE MOUTH T

ERECTNE AND RIGH Y SO MAKE

T YOU YES YOU LOOK NNIT LE

BELCEVE YOUR BOAT MORE E

CALOVE YOUR BOATNTINGEDING, C

THEN I DECIDED CEPTABLE B

UR BODY SHAPES TO MY OR OU

DOWN YOUR BOAT KISSERSX

4 MIN VID FOR MOR

PENIS TINUAL & FUCK-O-R

BEARDED LADY ALIVE IN M

"Skate around town at two in the morning in a suit don't give
a fuck drink a whole gallon of milk throw up don't listen to your
dad don't wash your hair or your clothes get cuts on your arms
and knees and never shave your whole face only parts of it and
bad haircuts are cool talk to pretty girls never sleep a wink in your
whole fucking life die at age thirty move to New York become an
investment banker destroy the world economy who cares lose
an eye in a knife fight eat ten whole pizzas puke ride a horse
live forever invent hyperdrive drop shitty Greenday CDs on the
beginnings of some alien civilization and ensure their demise
get sucked into a black hole meet god go skating watch him do
some gnarly creatorflips get stoned eat all of creation pass out and
repeat," the boy says.

"**Okay**," I say.

"I'm four hundred thousand years old I don't give a fuck anymore
I've lived through epochs and brought fire to man as Prometheus
and drank like Poseidon even with a crow tearing out my liver I
was Caesar selling daggers from a merch booth at the March fair
and in bloodshed I knew the glory of the ides my friend my friend
as a GOD I have lived but the nausea and hollow horror of the
Here and Now still brings me to fear and trembling my friend my
friend my dear Agamemnon do not forget that time is the horrid
dog Aegisthus who will betray the city and cut the fucking molly
with sleeping pills," says the boy with very greasy hair.

"**Oh**," I say.

"Have you looked upon the dome of heaven as I skate a wicked
50-50 precariously perched on the curve of gravitation are you
honestly happy existing on the face of god without the finest
virgin scenester girls oh my friend my friend I was happy once
when I nailed a five stair for the first time but that was billions
of years ago when the God King Marduk strode heavy across
the stars before I forsook the mortal realm and bought fake
Beats headphones and entered the lightless halls of inferior
sound quality and the dim peace of a sunless morn," says the
boy wearing a shirt that says only, "FUCK."

"**I have to go to class**."

"God spat on you when you were born and even modern monetary theory cannot reconcile the golden glorious power of me perching upon the edge of the fiscal cliff ready to drop in from non-Euclidean space and grind the cusps of a bitter cup that flew from my hand after I drank a billion ounces of lean and thrashed hard against sentimentality on the slopes of mount Olympus for it clogs the bearings of the board of modernity I will break that shit and hang it on my wall like a motherfucker I fucked a girl once in the back of a movie theater to 'Finding Nemo 3D' and bore the cosmos from the product of my thrusting hips," he says.

"I built a machine in my basement that will make all of the metal on earth disappear," I say.

He nods and we walk back to my house and activate the machine and all of the metal on earth disappears and we realize that this is impossible and that means something and he looks at me and says, "I don't know how to deal with any of this."

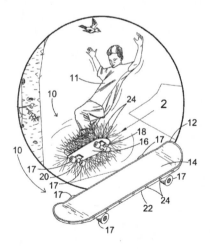

Face·book /fāsbŏŏk/: pixelated party place; purposelessly posting personal pictures presenting poorly parented pre-teens

sel·fie /selfē/: solo PDA

Ko·a·la Bears /kōˈälə/be(ə)rz/: not actually bears

Comparing Our Bodies

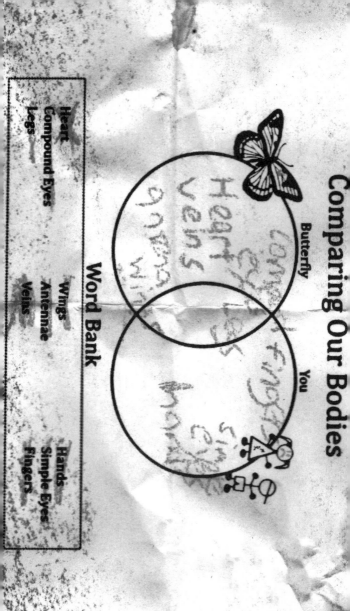

Butterfly

You

Heart
Veins
compound
wings

Fingers
simple
Hands

Word Bank

Heart
Compound Eyes
Legs

Wings
Antennae
Veins

Hands
Simple Eyes
Fingers

Dear Emiel,

I'm going to do a little experiment on you. I hope you don't mind. If you reject being used in my experiment you should stop reading right now! If you are still reading, you are a brave man! I like you, Emiel!

So, I'm going to try to hypnotize you. I've never done this before, but what harm is there in a little mesmerism? Maybe I'll become a mail order mesmerist. It's a little dream of mine. Are you ready, Emiel? Take out the polaroid I've enclosed.

Now, take a deep breath and stare into the stripes. Stare into the stripes, Emiel. Yes, just like that. You're really good at this!

Balthazar Simões

What thoughts are going through your mind? Perhaps you are thinking about the Higgs Boson? Or about your penis (those thoughts come up a lot!)? Or maybe about the weather (why are you thinking such boring thoughts as that, Emiel?)? I imagine that big, juicy steaks are floating through your mind (tasty meats are nice thoughts to have).

Now, I'm going to plant a thought into your mind. Keep staring at the stripes. Move your eyes just a bit lower, Emiel. Don't worry, it's OK. This is the word I want you to focus on while your eyes are mesmerized by the stripes (just a little lower now): mango. Let me repeat: mango. Can you feel the sweet, messy thoughts dripping on your brain? Mango. Please continue staring and concentrating on the word "mango" for 5 minutes. Let me know the results.

Yours,

Balthazar

PERSONALS

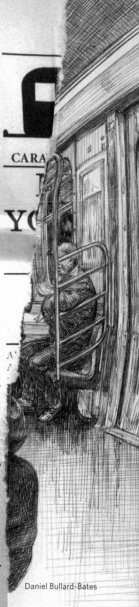

Muse wanted. Calliope preferred, Melpomene OK. MPDG may be acceptable. Must be available late nights and weekends. Offering worship, wine, honeyed milk, and a prominent place in the acknowledgements section.

Physically fit, motivated artist seeks same for position as primary nemesis. Should be faster, stronger, more talented. Looking to up my game.

SWM, late 20's, in the market for a wealthy, probably older patron. Gender and age are both negotiable. I'm not saying I will sleep with you, but I'm not saying I won't. Belief in my talent a definite plus.

POST
YOUR AD
HERE

Lazy but charming writer in search of editor/agent/friend to solve all my problems. You do all the work so I can focus on getting laid and trying every hallucinogen.

Me: stuck in windowless prison from 9 to 5 most weekdays. You: a team of quirky misfits with an elaborate escape plan. First we will escape the office, then the Beltway, material concerns, and suffering.

RADIO WAVES

There's this dance, it's called the Radio Wave and it's gotta beat that can't be beat. It's for the girls in flounced frocks and boys in shirtless ties and pointed Bruno Maglis. Fluent and fluid movements; cabaret style abandon in two and four time. They like it, and they like it a lot at the Down Beat, the Upstart, the Rock Bottom and the Hi-Hat.

With the Twisters at the T-table Bar they go man go. It's a crazy scene down there on Saturday nights. Makes you sweat just anticipating because you can't stop yourself when the Radio Wave hits. Pimple faced rowdies and grinders, the wannabe's and already ams, sauntering in from the periphery, asking the sexy girls to dance. And here's the thing about the Radio Wave – The girls can't say no, man. I've seen 'em, even the girls who are too pretty to dance. They're all breasts and legs, ponying up for a pint, whispering to the pretty girls who came with 'em; their bodies smug and resolute, disdainful of everyone but the young handsome banker in his banker suit doing the banker's nod and walking to the Radio Wave.

All they do is look, laugh and have their own fun. At least that was them until the Radio Wave. Now they are loose, and I mean loose if you know what I mean; dancing with just anyone.

But what a night! Let's go man! The pretty pretty girls, altruistic sexual philanthropists, just givin' it away when they dance the Radio Wave.

~~~~~~~~~~~~~~~~~~~~

We conceived of a name. It is the name we go by now. We are the full spectrum Radio Waves. We're everywhere and nowhere and no one sees us comin'. We do good and we do bad, but we do as we please. We are the coolest and the hottest. We are comin' and goin' at the same time. We're a damned conflagration, some kind of doppelganger effect gone subdural, if you know what I mean. We wear boots and Levi jeans, our hair greasy and slicked back. We wear it long over our ears and we don't listen to nobody but us.

Thom shot a man. Thom shot a man for nothing. That's the boy, Thom. Then he sucker kicked him in the ribs after the bastard took his last breath and, like the full spectrum punk he is, Thom goes off with this guy's old lady!

We are the full spectrum Radio Waves We rob. We steal and we beat shit outa helpless old men and little babies and cripples cause it's the baddest, it's the maddest and no else has ever thought of it. We shoot people, leavin' em with their breeches besmirched, we do. We use our looks, our full spectrum Radio Wave looks, and it beats them down. It beats them every time. Old ladies hand us their money; they give us the wheels off their wheelchairs...all in gratitude and hope.

What a world it is when you are a full spectrum Radio Wave... What a world!

~~~~~~~~~~~~~~~~

People are Radio Waving. Strangers, coworkers and the people you meet, just love to give you a great big Radio Wave when they pass by. It's a revolution. And the Radio Waves are here to stay. They are everywhere. Their wonderful lies and propaganda have taken over our country and half the world. They are ruining lives and committing necessary murder. They keep ruining lives and go on committing murder. They make us angry and they make us cry. We are visibly shaken; still we are happier than we have ever been. They are on television and in our radios. They are under our beds and on our roofs. They are in our hands and on our knees. Radio Waves are in our children's eyes, around their dirty little collars and integral parts of their futures; omnipresent, omniscient, omnipotent, omni this and omni that, just the way it always will be.

Can't you just see it? The comedians drinking beer in the morning and writing their jokes about the phenomenon of Radio Waves; about the new and better world being heralded by Radio Waves so pervasive that late night talk shows and CNN can speak to nothing but. How many Radio Waves to SCREW in a light bulb... Or get this, A Radio Wave walks into a bar, orders a drink... Knock, knock...Radio who?

We survivors are ourselves ablaze, roaring with laughter rolling on our living room floors and swerving in our automobiles. We're eating it up in the dance clubs and in our rampant unrepentant gangs. It can't be helped. It won't be stopped. It won't go away. Say it after me!
Radio Waves!
Radio Waves!
Now,

let's all get up and dance!

A Fiction Steve Vermillion

The Shy Prologue

Dear Reader,

We have an unfortunate talent for forgetting how amazing it is to be alive. I become aware sometimes that the bodily functions, the breathing, the hunger, even the petty dramas, are all pallid events compared to the miracle of my thinking about these things. I wonder then how reading fiction plays into it all. If each action we take is the result of a hunger, what hunger does reading fulfill?

Percy Shelley, my favorite atheist, writes:

Life and the world, or whatever we call that which we are and feel, is an astonishing thing. The mist of familiarity obscures from us the wonder of our being. We are struck with admiration at some of its transient modifications, but it is itself the great miracle. What are changes of empires, the wreck of dynasties, with the opinions which supported them; what is the birth and the extinction of religious and of political systems, to life? What are the revolutions of the globe which we inhabit, and the operations of the elements of which it is composed, compared with life? What is the universe of stars, and suns, of which this inhabited earth is one, and their motions, and their destiny, compared with life? Life, the great miracle, we admire not, because it is so miraculous. It is well that we are thus shielded by the familiarity of what is at once so certain and so unfathomable, from an astonishment which would otherwise absorb and overawe the functions of that which is its object.

This last part is key, I paraphrase and repeat: "We are thankfully shielded, most of the time, from the miracle of life. Otherwise, the unfathomable yet certain truth of life would overwhelm and break us." Does reading remind us of the miracle of life or separate us from it? Does reading induce these fits of wonder or simply stimulate them?

It is natural, right before going into or coming out of these fits of wonder, to experience some longing, some discontent, some unhappiness. You are forced to take a deep breath and accept the fact that you cannot sit on the porch all day ruminating on the nature of shadows.

Reading, at the heart of it, requires this unhappiness. To read calmly and peacefully, two things must be true in some degree: 1) You are not happy where you are and know there is something better to do, or see, or think about. 2) At such a time, your imagination is not energetic, creative, or organized enough to transport you without an aid. With these two truths, we may plunge into a story. We may, at a loss for something to ruminate on, sitting on a porch or elsewhere, use reading as a tool to inspire fits of wonder. The question is whether this experience and time spent reading is you experiencing the wonder of life or avoiding it.

For me, theNewerYork is my kickstarting device; a thing that reminds me how time works and moves, how quickly the narratives of life can shift. From wonder, to fear, to petty, to absurd, to mundane, to fantastic, to exciting, to boring, this book doesn't want me to read it, it wants me to put it down and go live; it alarms me.

If you'd like, you could spend two-weeks learning each aspect of these stories: every character, every joke, every hint, every trick. Like life, the brevity or length of the time you spend on it bears no relation to its depth. This book shows you that quick can also be deep, for it is the quality of time, not the length, that brings meaning to life. It only takes ten minutes sitting on a porch daydreaming to make up for a whole week of cubicle time. This book should remind you that two minutes spent on one page can bring you deeper than days spent on a novel.

Let these stories control you, let them take you places, bring you back, baffle you, and when you put the book down, realize that stories surround you.

Be alarmed,

JSR

Index

ART

BORSHCH, DMITRY

Dmitry Borshch is an American artist of Soviet origin. He was born in Dnepropetrovsk, studied in Moscow, today lives in New York and exhibits internationally. His work has been exhibited at the National Arts Club (NY), Brecht Forum (NY), Exit Art (NY), CUNY Graduate Center (NY), Salmagundi Club (NY), ISE Cultural Foundation (NY), Frieze Art Fair (London).
pages 11, 47

BOYD, ERIC

Eric Boyd is a dishwasher living in Pittsburgh, Pa. He briefly attended college at the Maharishi University of Management in Fairfield, Ia. A winner of the PEN American Center Prison Writing Award, Boyd has also been nominated for the Pushcart prize.
EricBoydblog.tumblr.com
page 57

DAVEY, NILS

Nils Davey is an art director, illustrator, graphic designer, and artist. His work can be found at http://www.nilsdavey.com
pages 4, 23, 35, 38

DE LAS HERAS, DAVID

I am an illustrator from Bilbao (Basque Country), but nowadays I am living and working in Barcelona, I work like a painter too.

My blog is:
http://carapajaro.blogspot.com.es/
and my facebook page:
http://www.facebook.com/
pages/David-de-las-Heras-
Ilustrador/332424243503275
my email is: dheras84@gmail.com
page 27

GORING, PENNY

Penny Goring lives in London
junktotem is an ongoing project documenting the junk she lives in
http://www.junktotem.com/
http://pjgoring.tumblr.com/
twitter@triplecherry
page 53

LIPMAN, STEPHEN

Stephen Lipman was born and raised in the Bronx, New York City and his studio is in the Bronx. He received a B.F.A. in Fine Art and Philosophy from Manhattan College, NY and continued his education at the Art Students League and the Spring Street Studio, NY. His work was exhibited most recently at the AC Institute, 547 W 27th St. #210, NYC
page 18

MAER, THOKA

166cm high, 54kg heavy, held together by skin, decorated with hair, and usually framed in the city known as Berlin. hello@thokamaer.com, thokamaer.com twitter: @thokamaer
page 33

MEERWEH

meerweh - the Illustrator Nadine Kappacher - lives and works in Vienna, Austria. More about her work: meerweh.tumblr.com / portfolio: meerweh.carbonmade.com /contact: nadine.kappacher@gmx.at
page 58

SOBIESKI, ANIELA

Aniela Sobieski is a Minnesota based artist who creates small scale paintings of dream-like subjects. Her paintings often feature human-animal hybrids, speaking to the fluid nature of identity. She has participated in exhibitions nationally and internationally. She currently lives in Syracuse, NY where she is persuing an MFA in painting.
page 7

NELSON, LORI

Lori is a Brooklyn-based artist who likes to paint about people who feel like they're dying in social situations. She also likes to paint about the Internet. You should see. www.lorinelson.com
page 29

PARK, GUNO

www.gunopark.com
page 62

TADIC, MARKO

Marko Tadic is an artist living
in Croatia. His work spans many
mediums and has been featured
in publications and galleries around
the world. See his more of his art at
http://markotadic.blogspot.com/
and contact him at
markotadik@gmail.com
page 40

YANG, ALISA

Alisa Yang received her BFA with
honors from Art Center College
of Design in 2009. She currently
works as a curator at Gemini G.E.L
and as a contributing illustrator for
Artillery magazine. She has exhibited
at Mckinley Art and Culture Center
in Reno, Another Year in LA gallery,
Gallery 825, University of North
Dakota, the Los Angeles Municipal
Art Gallery, and the Riverside Art
Museum. Yang has been reviewed in
the LA Times, Fabrik magazine, and
the Huffington Post. More works at
www.AlisaYang.com
page 25

AUTHORS

BLACHMAN, JEREMY

Jeremy Blachman is a published novelist (Anonymous Lawyer, Henry Holt; developed for television by Sony and NBC) with humor pieces published by The Wall Street Journal, McSweeney's Internet Tendency, The New Republic, Barnes and Noble's Grin & Tonic and more. Follow him @jeremyblachman or read more at jeremyblachman.com
page 36

BULLARD-BATES, DANIEL

If he were in a post-apocalyptic wasteland gang, Daniel Bullard-Bates would shave his head and grow out his beard. Contact: dbullardbates@gmail.com
page 60

CHRISTMASS, SHANE JESSE

Shane Jesse Christmass is an Australian writer. He's a member of the band Mattress Grave, and firmly believes that the future of the word, the novel, will be in synthetic telepathy. Website: luparapublishing.blogspot.com.au/ Facebook/Twitter: SJXSJC https://vimeo.com/sjx
page 28

CHRISTOPHERSON, BRYCE A.

Bryce Christopherson is an average quality robot from Sioux Falls, South Dakota. You can follow him on twitter at @brycechristoph
page 54

COCOTAS, ALEX

Alex Cocotas is a writer living in Brooklyn. You can reach him at acocotas@gmail.com or ranting at alexcocotas.tumblr.com.
page 48

DAVIDSON, ZACH

Zach Davidson is a writer who is located in Toronto but who spends most of his time in his head. He writes on a variety of subjects, in a variety of forms, using a variety of page lengths. His email is: zach.n.davidson@gmail.com
page 52

DeLashmutt, A. C.

My favorite word is eyrie, when it's spoken aloud, so that it can mean both "the lofty nest of a bird of prey" and irie, "a state of total peace and harmony."
ACDeLashmutt@gmail.com
page 19

Gosnay, Christine

Christine Gosnay has recent poetry in DIAGRAM, Beecher's Magazine, Amethyst Arsenic, and Cactus Heart. She is the editor of The Cossack Review and can be found on twitter @dagny and at sandwich shops worldwide arguing about how to make the perfect ALT.
page 14

Holdefer, Charles

Charles Holdefer is an American writer currently based in Brussels. He has published four novels, most recently "Back in the Game" (2012). His work appeared in the New England Review, North American Review, Slice and other magazines. Website: charlesholdefer.com
page 16

HUFFMAN, JANE

Jane Huffman is a Michigan-based writer with works featured or forthcoming in Thought Catalog, Galavant Magazine, and A Bad Penny Review. http://janehuffman.blogspot.com/
page 8

JULIEN, HEIKO

Heiko Julien is an artist from Chicago. His book 'I Am Ready to Die a Violent Death' will be out this summer. Website: facebook.com/helloimfinehowareyou
page 32

KEATING, JOHN

John Keating lives in Cork, Ireland, where he co-edits The Penny Dreadful literary magazine.
page 2

NACHMAN, GIDEON

Gideon Nachman is from Brooklyn, New York, originally, but currently lives outside of Boston. He's a student for now, and uses improv comedy as his free therapy. He is told on an almost-daily basis that he 'looks Mediterranean'. He has no Mediterranean ancestry. He can be reached at gwn888@gmail.com
page 6

NIMBLETT, ANTON

Anton Nimblett, a Trinidadian who lives and writes in Brooklyn, is the author of Sections of an Orange, a collection of short stories published by Peepal Tree Press. His fiction appears in the award-winning anthology Our Caribbean. His poetry is included in War Diaries, an anthology; literary review and verse appear in sx salon. Anton thinks that writing is the best therapy for the madness that is writing. Website: sectionsofanorange.com
page 44